THE ULTIMATE LEICESTER FC TRIVIA BOOK

A Collection of Amazing Trivia Quizzes and Fun Facts for Die-Hard Foxes Fans!

Ray Walker

978-1-953563-70-5

Exclusive Free Book

Crazy Sports Stories

As a thank you for getting a copy of this book I would like to offer you a free copy of my book Crazy Sports Stories which comes packed with interesting stories from your favorite sports such as Football, Hockey, Baseball, Basketball and more.

Grab your free copy over at

RayWalkerMedia.com/Bonus

CONTENTS

INTRODUCTION

Leicester City FC has progressed over the years from a bible class and schoolyard chums to being one of England's most famous and entertaining soccer clubs. Now nicknamed the Foxes, the club originated back in 1884 as Leicester Fosse, and currently holds the nation's record for second-tier titles, not to mention shocking the sports world by hoisting the 2015-16 Premier League championship against all odds.

The side has also endured some unpleasant times as well, such as a dozen relegations throughout history and the tragic death of owner Khun Vichai Srivaddhanaprabha, in October 2018 after he took off in a helicopter from the King Power Stadium pitch.

Foxes' fans have been packing grounds from Victoria Park to Grace Road Cricket Ground to Filbert Street and King Power Stadium to see their favorite team in action week after week.

The squad's never-say-die attitude is well known throughout the soccer world, and this has resulted in its fair share of silverware, and a thoroughly intriguing history.

Leicester supporters have had the great fortune of witnessing some of the world's most skilled, and hardest-working players, grace the pitch over the past century such as Graham Cross, Adam Black, Steve Walsh, Jamie Vardy, Kasper Schmeichel, Wes Morgan, Mal Griffiths, Sep Smith, Don Revie, Peter Hodge, Matt Gillies, Claudio Ranieri, Gordon Banks, Peter Shilton, Gary Lineker, Arthur Rowley, Muzzy Izzet, Paul Dickov, Len Glover, David Nish, N'Golo Kanté, Frank Sinclair, and Shinji Okazaki.

This trivia book was written to celebrate the club's colorful history by telling the Leicester story from day one right up until April 2021. You'll be able to meet the side's most beloved players and managers while learning how each of them affected the club in his own unique way.

The Foxes' history is presented here in entertaining quiz form with 12 unique chapters, each on a different topic. Each section includes 20 electrifying quiz questions along with 10 exhilarating "Did you Know" facts. The questions are presented as 15 multiple-choice and 5 true-or-false options, with the correct answers revealed on a separate page.

We feel this is the ideal way to challenge and test yourself on the wonderful history of Leicester FC, and then to take on fellow fans in lighthearted trivia contests.

The book was written to help refresh your knowledge and memory of your favorite team through the peaks and valleys, and to help you prepare for all trivia challenges that come your way.

Thanks, and good luck!

CHAPTER 1:

ORIGINS & HISTORY

QUIZ TIME!

1. What year was the club founded?

    a. 1894
    b. 1890
    c. 1884
    d. 1880

2. The first time a crest was featured on a shirt was in 1952.

    a. True
    b. False

3. What was the club's original name?

    a. Leicester Football and Cricket Boys Club
    b. Filbert Foxes FC
    c. Leicester Athletic
    d. Leicester Fosse

4. Which color was Leicester's original shirt?

    a. Black
    b. Green and white stripes

c. Yellow
d. Royal blue and white stripes

5. What is Leicester's nickname?

a. The Blues
b. The Foxes
c. Odd Dogs
d. The Hunters

6. Which major league did Leicester first play in?

a. The Combination
b. The Football League
c. The Midland League
d. The Football Alliance

7. Leicester was a founding member of the English Premier League.

a. True
b. False

8. the Foxes first recorded match was a 5-0 victory over which club?

a. Birmingham City FC
b. Syston Fosse
c. Nottingham Forest FC
d. Glenfield Athletics

9. Where did Leicester play its home games between 1891 and 2002?

a. Filbert Street
b. Victoria Park

c. Mill Lane
d. Fosse Road

10. How many times has the side been relegated as of 2020?

a. 5
b. 7
c. 8
d. 12

11. Which club did the Foxes play in their first Football League game?

a. Grimsby Town FC
b. Lincoln City FC
c. Newton Heath
d. Woolwich Arsenal

12. Leicester was first relegated to the Second Division in 1908-09.

a. True
b. False

13. How many matches did the team win in its first season in the Midland League?

a. 3
b. 5
c. 10
d. 16

14. Leicester played which club in its first Premier League game?

a. Everton FC
b. Nottingham Forest FC
c. Blackburn Rovers FC
d. Newcastle United

15. What was the first year the Foxes competed for the FA Cup?

a. 1899-00
b. 1894-95
c. 1890-91
d. 1888-89

16. Julian Joachim scored the club's first goal in the Premier League.

a. True
b. False

17. How many games did the squad win in its first English Football League campaign?

a. 6
b. 10
c. 13
d. 15

18. the Foxes beat which outfit to win their first Premier League match?

a. Queens Park Rangers
b. Arsenal FC
c. Southampton FC
d. Tottenham Hotspur

19. How many games did Leicester win in its first Premier League season?

    a. 11
    b. 9
    c. 6
    d. 4

20. One of Leicester's original nicknames was the Fossils.

    a. True
    b. False

QUIZ ANSWERS

1. C – 1884
2. B – False
3. D – Leicester Fosse
4. A – Black
5. B – the Foxes
6. C – The Midland League
7. B – False
8. B – Syston Fosse
9. A – Filbert Street
10. D – 12
11. A – Grimsby Town FC
12. A – True
13. B – 5
14. D – Newcastle United
15. C – 1890-91
16. A – True
17. D – 15
18. D – Tottenham Hotspur
19. C – 6
20. A – True

DID YOU KNOW?

1. Leicester City Football Club currently competes in the English Premier League and plays its home matches at the King Power Stadium in the city of Leicester. The club was founded in 1884 as Leicester Fosse FC and is nicknamed the Foxes.

2. The roots of the club can be traced to a bible class at the former Emanuel Chapel on New Park Street, Leicester. Many members had attended Wyggeston School together and Reverend Lewellyn H. Parsons taught the bible studies. The Fosse Way was the name of an old Roman thoroughfare that linked the southwest of England to the northeast.

3. Leicester Fosse's first recorded match was held on Nov. 1, 1884, on a private pitch and resulted in a 5-0 win over Syston Fosse. The average age of the squad was just 16. Arthur West and Hilton Johnson each scored twice, and Sam Dingley tallied once.

4. The team played at Victoria Park between 1884 and 1887 and planned to move to the Belgrave Road Cycle and Cricket Ground in 1888 but the Leicester Tigers Rugby Club outbid them for the venue. The side returned to Victoria Park and eventually moved to Mill Lane.

5. At that time, the club's nickname was the Fossils, or the Ancients, and the first piece of silverware was won when

they beat Coalville in the Leicestershire County Cup final, in Loughborough in 1890. The team then played in the FA Cup for the first time the next season.

6. When the city began to build homes on Mill Lane, the club moved to the Grace Road Cricket Ground for a brief time. In October 1891, it moved to Filbert Street, to a venue that was known as the Walnut Street Ground, and the team played in the Midland League. The venue soon became known as Filbert Street Stadium.

7. The club was elected to the recently formed Second Division of the Football League in 1894 and wore a black strip with a sky-blue sash and long white shorts. However, they soon changed to a shirt that featured chocolate brown and blue halves before deciding to wear royal blue and white in 1903.

8. The side's first Football League match was a 4-3 loss at Grimsby Town, with the first victory coming the following week at Filbert Street, against Rotherham United. The same season, the Foxes hammered Notts Olympic 13-0 in an FA Cup qualifying game to record its biggest ever win.

9. It took Leicester Fosse over a decade to earn promotion to the First Division as it achieved the feat by finishing as Second Division runners-up in 1907-08. However, they were relegated back to the second tier after just one season, and also suffered their worst defeat ever, a 12-0 beat down by Nottingham Forest.

10. The club struggled financially at this time, and the Football League was suspended in April 1915 due to World War I. Since the team had finished second-last in the Second Division that season, it had to be re-elected to remain in the Football League. After the war, the club was still struggling financially in 1918 and it was taken over by a new company that was registered as Leicester City Football Club in 1919.

CHAPTER 2:

THE CAPTAIN CLASS

QUIZ TIME!

1. Who captained the Foxes during their first season in the Premier League?
   a. Scott Eustace
   b. Gary Mills
   c. Richard Smith
   d. Simon Grayson
2. Matt Mills captained the Foxes to their first Premier League title.
   a. True
   b. False
3. Which club did Paddy McCarthy captain after he left Leicester?
   a. Leeds United
   b. Wolverhampton Wanderers
   c. Preston North End
   d. Crystal Palace

4. Who captained the club to its first Second Division title?

   a. Johnny Duncan
   b. Sep Smith
   c. Arthur Chandler
   d. Alex Trotter

5. How many trophies has Wes Morgan captained Leicester to?

   a. 6
   b. 3
   c. 2
   d. 0

6. Matt Oakley captained which club before he joined the Foxes?

   a. Derby County FC
   b. Wigan Athletic
   c. Brighton Hove and Albion
   d. Blackburn Rovers FC

7. Wes Morgan has won the club's Player of the Year award five times since being named captain.

   a. True
   b. False

8. Steve Walsh took over the captaincy from this player.

   a. Ally Mauchlen
   b. Gary Parker
   c. Gary Mills
   d. David Speedie

9. Who captained the Foxes to their first League Cup trophy in 1963-64?

    a. Matt Elliot
    b. Ken Keyworth
    c. Steve Walsh
    d. Colin Appleton

10. Ally Mauchlen skippered which Scottish club before joining Leicester?

    a. Gretna FC
    b. Kilmarnock FC
    c. Motherwell FC
    d. Aberdeen FC

11. Who wore the armband in the 1970-71 Second Division title-winning season?

    a. David Nish
    b. Steve Whitworth
    c. Keith Weller
    d. Bobby Kellard

12. Matt Elliot won the club's Player of the Year award in his first season with Leicester.

    a. True
    b. False

13. Who did Wes Morgan Succeed as captain?

    a. Dany N'Guessan
    b. Matt Mills

c. Kasper Schmeichel
d. Matt Oakley

14. Which club did Danny Tiatto leave before becoming captain of the Foxes?

a. Melbourne Knights
b. Chelsea FC
c. Wolverhampton Wanderers
d. Manchester City

15. What was Steve Walsh's nickname?

a. Sir Walsh
b. Captain Fantastic
c. The Leader of Leicester
d. Captain Fantasy

16. Kasper Schmeichel captained the Foxes between 2015-16 and 2016-17.

a. True
b. False

17. Matt Mills captained which club after he left Leicester?

a. Sunderland AFC
b. Manchester City
c. Southampton FC
d. Nottingham Forest FC

18. Who captained the club to victory in Leicester's only season in the third-tier English Football League One Division?

a. Danny Tiatto
b. Paddy McCarthy

c. Matt Oakley
d. Stephen Clemence

19. Who took over the armband from Steve Walsh?

a. Matt Elliot
b. Robbie Savage
c. Tony Cottee
d. Frank Sinclair

20. Gary Mills was Leicester's first captain born outside of the British Isles.

a. True
b. False

QUIZ ANSWERS

1. B – Gary Mills
2. B – False
3. D – Crystal Palace
4. A – Johnny Duncan
5. C – 2
6. A – Derby County FC
7. B – False
8. B – Gary Parker
9. D – Colin Appleton
10. C – Motherwell FC
11. A – David Nish
12. A – True
13. B – Matt Mills
14. D – Manchester City
15. B – Captain Fantastic
16. B – False
17. D – Nottingham Forest FC
18. C – Matt Oakley
19. A – Matt Elliot
20. B – False

DID YOU KNOW?

1. Forward Johnny Duncan of Scotland, who was nicknamed "Tokey", captained the club to the Second Division title in 1924-25, as well as to third and second place finishes in the First Division, in 1927-28 and 1928-29, respectively. He managed the club between 1946 and 1949. Duncan shares the club record with Arthur Chandler for the most goals in a game, with perhaps his most memorable game coming when he tallied 6 in a 7-0 win over Port Vale on Christmas Day in 1924. Duncan joined the Foxes in 1922 from Raith Rovers, playing until 1930, and scoring 95 goals scored in just under 300 games.
2. Known as the Foxes' longest-serving player, Septimus "Sep" Smith was also one of the club's longest-serving skippers. The midfielder and forward was with the side for 19 years and 246 days, wearing the armband for 13 years. He spent his entire career at Filbert Street between 1929-1949 and made 373 straight competitive appearances while chipping in with 37 goals. He also played 213 unofficial games during World War II. Smith skippered the side to the 1936-37 Second Division crown and was the guest of honor at the team's final game at Filbert Street. There's now a suite named after him at King Power Stadium.
3. Defender Matt Gillies captained the squad to a dramatic Second Division title in 1953-54 as the club topped the table

by goal difference over Everton with third-place Blackburn Rovers just a point behind. Gillies of Scotland later managed the Foxes for a club-record 508 games between 1958 and 1968. He made 111 appearances as a player, after arriving in January 1952 from Bolton Wanderers where he was club captain, and he played his final three seasons with Leicester.

4. English international winger Jack Froggatt wore the armband for Leicester when they won the Second Division title in 1956-57. He joined the side from Portsmouth in March 1954 and played 143 matches for the Foxes while contributing 18 goals before leaving in 1957 for Kettering Town, where he became player and manager. Froggatt's uncle Frank and cousin Redfern Froggatt both played for Sheffield Wednesday. Known as "Jolly Jack", Froggatt's 20-year career came to an end in May 1963, and he then operated a pub in Portsmouth.

5. Leicester's first League Cup triumph came in 1963-64 with skipper Colin Appleton leading the side to a 4-3 aggregate victory against Stoke City. He arrived in March 1954 from Scarborough just after turning 18 years old. Appleton also helped the side win the 1956-57 Second Division title and reach the 1960-61 FA Cup final against Tottenham Hotspur. The team then chased the FA Cup and League double in 1962-63, but it came to nothing as the club finished fourth in the league and was downed 3-1 by Manchester United in the FA Cup final. Appleton then led the Foxes to the 1964-1965 League Cup final where they

were edged by Chelsea 3-2 on aggregate. He played 333 official games with the side before joining Charlton Athletic in 1966.

6. Leicester won the Second Division title for the fifth time with David Nish as skipper, and then entered the FA Charity Shield in 1971, since Arsenal won the First Division and FA Cup double. The Foxes then surprised FA Cup finalists Liverpool by winning the charity match 1-0 at Filbert Street. The English international defender kicked off his pro career with Leicester from 1966 to 1972 and tallied 31 goals in 273 outings. Derby County paid a then-record transfer fee of £225,000 for him, and Nish helped the team win the First Division in 1974-75. He later moved to America to play.

7. Goalkeeper Mark Wallington wore the club's armband in 1979-1980 when yet another Second Division title was secured by a lone point over Sunderland. Wallington currently holds the club record for appearances by a keeper with 460. He arrived in March 1972 from Walsall and stayed until 1985 when he joined Derby County. He was acquired to back up Peter Shilton and then took over the top job when Shilton joined Stoke City in 1974. Wallington once played 331 straight games and was named to the PFA Second Division Team of the Year for 1978-79 and 1981-82.

8. The 1996-97 League Cup triumph in a replay over Middlesbrough came with defender Steve Walsh as

skipper, and he was also named man of the match. The club won the playoffs a year earlier in extra time against Crystal Palace to return to the top flight and Walsh was also with the team when they won the 1993-94 playoffs, and the 1999-2000 League Cup. The defender occasionally played as a striker, and shares a record with Roy McDonough for receiving 13 red cards in the English Football League. He arrived from Wigan Athletic in 1986 and was given the armband in 1992, he also wore it in the 1998-99 League Cup final loss to Tottenham Hotspur. Nicknamed "Captain Fantastic", Walsh joined Norwich City in 2000 after netting 52 goals in 450 appearances.

9. Captain Matt Elliott helped the side win the 1999-2000 League Cup by scoring both goals in the 2-1 win over Tranmere Rovers at Wembley and being named man of the match. The Scottish international defender joined from Oxford United in 1997 and played the final eight years of his career with the Foxes but spent part of 2004 on loan with Ipswich Town. He also helped the team reach the 1998-99 League Cup final and finish as second-tier First Division runners-up in 2002-03. Elliot retired in January 2005 after scoring 33 times in 290 outings with the squad.

10. English-born Jamaican international defender Wes Morgan captained the team to the 2013-14 second-tier Championship League crown and the 2015-16 Premier League title. Morgan arrived from Nottingham Forest in January 2012 and was given the armband shortly afterward. He was the first Jamaican international to score

in a European Champions League and was named to the PFA Championship Team of the Year for 2012-13 and 2013-14 with the Foxes as well as the PFA Premier League Team of the Year for 2015-16. Morgan was also named to the Football League Team of the Decade for 2005-2015 and won the Leicester Player of the Season and Players' Player of the Season for 2012-13. He was still with the club as of April 2021 and had played over 320 games with the team.

CHAPTER 3:

AMAZING MANAGERS

QUIZ TIME!

1. Who was regarded as the first official full-time manager of Leicester?
   a. Arthur Lochhead
   b. Willie Orr
   c. John W. Bartlett
   d. Peter Hodge
2. Up until 1919, Leicester was primarily managed by a committee, which was overseen by a secretary/manager.
   a. True
   b. False
3. How many full-time Leicester managers hailed from outside of the British Isles?
   a. 1
   b. 2
   c. 4
   d. 6

4. Who managed the Foxes to their first-ever FA Cup final appearance?
    a. Tom Mather
    b. Norman Bullock
    c. Johnny Duncan
    d. Tom Bromilow
5. Which season did Nigel Pearson win the LMA Championship Manager of the Year award?
    a. 2013-14
    b. 2011-12
    c. 2009-10
    d. 2007-08
6. Martin O'Neill left which club to join the Foxes?
    a. Norwich City FC
    b. Aston Villa
    c. Fulham FC
    d. Notts County FC
7. Matt Gillies managed over 600 matches with Leicester.
    a. True
    b. False
8. In terms of the number of team trophies won, who is the Foxes' most successful manager?
    a. Matt Gillies
    b. Nigel Pearson
    c. Martin O'Neill
    d. Claudio Ranieri

9. Which club did Paulo Sousa leave to join Leicester?

    a. Sporting CP
    b. Braga FC
    c. Swansea City FC
    d. Stoke City FC

10. Who was the first Foxes manager to hail from outside of the British Isles?

    a. Paulo Sousa
    b. Claudio Ranieri
    c. Sven-Göran Eriksson
    d. Claude Puel

11. Which national team did Sven-Göran Eriksson not manage?

    a. Mexico
    b. England
    c. Ivory Coast
    d. Republic of Ireland

12. Colin Appleton took over as player-manager from 1962-63 to 1964-65.

    a. True
    b. False

13. After his second stint with the Foxes ended, Nigel Pearson managed which club?

    a. Sunderland AFC
    b. Derby County FC

c. Stoke City FC
d. Queens Park Rangers

14. How many trophies did Claudio Ranieri win with the team?

a. 4
b. 1
c. 6
d. 3

15. Which full-time boss did Brendan Rogers replace in February 2019?

a. Garry Parker
b. Henry Jackson
c. Craig Shakespeare
d. Claude Puel

16. Mark McGhee was the Foxes' manager in their first season in the Premier League.

a. True
b. False

17. How many trophies did Martin O'Neill win managing Leicester?

a. 5
b. 3
c. 2
d. 0

18. In which country was Claude Puel born?

a. France
b. Spain
c. Brazil
d. Andorra

19. Micky Adams was manager of what club before he took over at Leicester?

    a. Preston North End
    b. Fulham FC
    c. Port Vale FC
    d. Brighton Hove and Albion

20. Sven-Göran Eriksson was the first foreign-born manager of the English men's national team.

    a. True
    b. False

QUIZ ANSWERS

1. D – Peter Hodge
2. A – True
3. C – 4
4. C – Johnny Duncan
5. A – 2013-14
6. A – Norwich City FC
7. B – False
8. C – Martin O'Neill
9. C – Swansea City FC
10. A – Paulo Sousa
11. D – Republic of Ireland
12. B – False
13. B – Derby County FC
14. A – 1
15. D – Claude Puel
16. B – False
17. C – 2
18. A – France
19. D – Brighton Hove and Albion
20. A – True

DID YOU KNOW?

1. The club reportedly had no official manager until after World War I when Peter Hodge was hired for the role. Until then, the Leicester board of directors employed a secretary/manager, and the selection committee controlled most team affairs. Hodge implemented a system that gave the club manager complete control over team selection, tactics, and player and staff recruitment.
2. According to Leicester City's official website, since 1884 the club has appointed a total of 47 permanent secretary/managers and managers. Former bosses Nigel Pearson and Peter Hodge have both had two separate stints with the team. In addition, Dave Bassett had a second stint as caretaker manager after a spell as permanent manager.
3. All but four of Leicester's managers came from England, Scotland, Northern Ireland, or the Republic of Ireland. Paulo Sousa hailed from Portugal, Sven-Göran Eriksson came from Sweden, Claudio Ranieri hailed from Italy, and Claude Puel was French.
4. The only two Leicester managers to win the Manager of the Year award from the League Managers' Association so far have been Nigel Pearson, in the second-tier Championship League for 2013-2014, and Claudio Ranieri for the Premier League and the best overall manager for 2015-2016. Ranieri also won the Best FIFA Men's Coach Award for 2015-16.

5. From 1884 to 1892, Frank Gardner was considered the driving force behind the club from day one. He played with the team and was its first secretary. Gardner helped the side in establishing a permanent home at Filbert Street in 1891, and in joining the Football League in 1894. He signed the club's first professional player, Harry Webb from Stafford Rangers, and entered the team in the Leicestershire Challenge Cup in 1888-89, the Leicestershire Senior Cup in 1890, and the FA Cup in 1890-91. By the time the side entered the Midland League in 1891, it had 12 professional players and had moved to Filbert Street.

6. Peter Hodge of Scotland was in charge from 1919 to 1926 and 1932 to 1934. He was the first boss after the club became Leicester City FC. He previously worked with Raith Rovers and Stoke City, and was a recruitment officer during World War I. Hodge guided the team to the Second Division title in 1924-25 and signed some of the team's earliest stars, including Adam Black, Johnny Duncan, Arthur Chandler, Hughie Adcock, Ernie Hine, Reg Osborne, and Arthur Lochhead. After just one season in the top flight, Hodge joined Manchester City, but returned to the Foxes in 1932 and reached the Club's first FA Cup semi-final in 1934. Sadly, he passed away in August 1934 at the age of 63 while still club manager.

7. Leicester's first manager to hail from outside the British Isles was Paulo Sousa of Portugal, but his tenure was short-lived. He was appointed in July 2010 to take over from Nigel Pearson, who had joined Hull City a month

earlier. Sousa was a former Portuguese international player and won several team trophies during his club career with different European teams. He hung up his boots at the age of 31 due to injuries and entered coaching in 2005-06. After stints with Queens Park Rangers and Swansea City, he joined the Foxes, but lasted just a few months after winning only one of his first nine games.

8. Matt Gillies of Scotland was one of the longest-serving managers, as he was in charge between 1958 and 1968 and handled the most games at the club with over 500. The former captain of Bolton Wanderers signed for Leicester in January 1952 for £9,500, and helped the side win the Second Division title in 1953-54. He joined the team's coaching staff in 1956 and the side won the Second Division title again the next season. Gillies became acting manager in November 1958 and was named permanent boss two months later. The team reached the FA Cup final in 1960-61 and 1962-63, won the League Cup in 1963-64, and reached the League Cup final again in 1964-65 before Gillies left in November 1968.

9. Claudio Ranieri will forever be a Leicester legend as he guided the squad to the 2015-16 Premier League by 10 points while losing just three games. He also won several individual awards that season and was inducted into the Italian Football Hall of Fame. Ranieri was hired in July 2015 to little fanfare since his side had lost to the Faroe Islands when he was managing the Greek national men's team. In fact, he had already managed 14 clubs before

arriving in Leicester. His original goal for 2015-16 was to earn 40 points and remain in the top flight. But the stars aligned, and the team continued to gain momentum. His side made it to the quarterfinals of the European Champions League the next season but, with the team struggling in the Premier League, he left King Power Stadium in February 2017.

10. While Leicester may not have always performed that well in the league for manager Martin O'Neill of Northern Ireland, the side was excellent in the League Cup. The former international captain won several team trophies during his top-flight club career before entering management. He was appointed Leicester boss in December 1995 and won just 3 of his first 16 matches. However, a late-season surge saw the club reach the second-tier playoffs, with the Foxes scoring a late goal in the final, to secure promotion to the Premier League. Over the next four seasons, the team won the League Cup in 1996-97 and 1999-200 while losing the 1998-99 final. The team also qualified twice for the UEFA Cup. O'Neill then left to manage Glasgow Celtic in June 2000.

CHAPTER 4:

GOALTENDING GREATS

QUIZ TIME!

1. Which keeper made the most appearances for Leicester?
    a. Gordon Banks
    b. Mark Wallington
    c. Peter Shilton
    d. Kasey Keller
2. Gordon Banks is the only player to have won the World Cup while playing for the Foxes.
    a. True
    b. False
3. How many clean sheets did Ian Walker keep in the 2002-03 domestic league season?
    a. 10
    b. 15
    c. 19
    d. 22

4. Who backed up Paul Henderson in 18 games in the 2006-07 Championship League?
   a. Conrad Logan
   b. Ben Alnwick
   c. Kevin Pressman
   d. Ian Walker
5. How many appearances did Peter Shilton make in all competitions with the Foxes?
   a. 378
   b. 340
   c. 327
   d. 295
6. Who played in goal for the Foxes' first-ever Premier League match?
   a. Pegguy Arphexad
   b. Kevin Poole
   c. Kasey Keller
   d. Gavin Ward
7. David Martin made 30 appearances in the 2008-09 League One season.
   a. True
   b. False
8. Which club did Peter Shilton join after leaving Leicester?
   a. Chelsea FC
   b. Valencia CF

c. Stoke City FC
d. SV Werder Bremen

9. Which player made 45 appearances in the 2009-10 domestic league?

a. Chris Kirkland
b. David Stockdale
c. Chris Weale
d. Mark Bunn

10. How many times was Gordon Banks capped by the English men's national team while playing with the Foxes?

a. 26
b. 37
c. 55
d. 72

11. Ian Walker joined the Foxes from which side?

a. Leeds United
b. Tottenham Hotspur
c. Manchester City
d. Newcastle United

12. Kasper Schmeichel finished third in voting for the 2018 Best FIFA Goalkeeper award.

a. True
b. False

13. How many appearances did Mark Wallington make for the Foxes?

a. 374
b. 389
c. 422
d. 460

14. Paul Cooper left the Foxes for which outfit in March 1989?

    a. Queens Park Rangers
    b. Manchester City
    c. Peterborough United
    d. Nottingham Forest FC

15. How many clean sheets did Mark Wallington keep for the club?

    a. 140
    b. 115
    c. 134
    d. 128

16. Gordon Banks won the FIFA Goalkeeper of the Year award four times while with Leicester.

    a. True
    b. False

17. Who backed up Kasper Schmeichel in 9 matches in the 2016-17 Premier League campaign?

    a. Ron-Robert Zieler
    b. Mark Schwarzer
    c. Ben Hamer
    d. Eldin Jakupović

18. How many appearances did Gordon Banks make with Leicester?

    a. 440
    b. 392
    c. 356
    d. 342

19. Which player made 22 appearances in the 2000-01 Premier League?

    a. Kasey Keller
    b. Pegguy Arphexad
    c. Simons Royce
    d. Tim Flowers

20. Kevin Poole posted over 100 clean sheets with the Foxes.

    a. True
    b. False

QUIZ ANSWERS

1. B – Mark Wallington
2. A – True
3. C – 19
4. A – Conrad Logan
5. B – 340
6. D – Gavin Ward
7. B – False
8. C – Stoke City FC
9. C – Chris Weale
10. B – 37
11. B – Tottenham Hotspur
12. A – True
13. D – 460
14. B – Manchester City
15. D – 128
16. B – False
17. A – Ron-Robert Zieler
18. C – 356
19. D – Tim Flowers
20. B – False

DID YOU KNOW?

1. When it comes to keeping clean sheets with the Foxes, here are the top 10 goalkeepers: Kasper Schmeichel, 133 in 415 games; Mark Wallington, 128 in 460 games; Peter Shilton, 116 in 340 games; Gordon Banks, 84 in 356 games; Johnny Anderson, 58 in 277 games; Sandy McLaren, 55 in 256 games; Herbert Bown, 52 in 154 games; Kasey Keller, 46 in 125 games; Ian Walker, 44 in 156 games; and Kevin Poole, 43 in 193 games. It should be noted that Schmeichel was still playing with Leicester as of April 2021.

2. Several Foxes' goalkeepers managed to post clean sheets in 50 percent or more of their games but none of them made more than 14 appearances. The best clean sheet percentages for players who appeared in over 50 games with the team are as follows: Godfrey Beardsley, 33 in 76 for 43.42%; George Hebden, 39 in 104 for 37.50%; Kasey Keller, 46 in 125 for 36.80%; Albert Godderidge, 20 in 56 for 35.71%; Peter Shilton, 116 in 340 for 34.12%; Paul Henderson, 25 in 74 for 33.78%; Herbert Bown, 52 in 154 for 33.77%; Walter Smith, 28 in 87 for 32.18%; Kasper Schmeichel, 133 in 415 for 32.05%; Paul Cooper, 22 in 70 for 31.43%.

3. Legendary English international Gordon Banks is considered by many experts to be one of the greatest keepers ever. He led England to the 1966 World Cup, and

is the only Leicester player to have won the trophy while playing with the club. He played with the team from 1959 to 1967 after signing from Chesterfield. Banks played in the 1960-61 and 1962-63 FA Cup finals, won the 1963-64 League Cup, and played the 1964-65 League Cup final. He left for Stoke City and then lost the sight in one eye following a 1972 car crash. However, he played for the Fort Lauderdale Strikers in 1977 and was named the NASL Goalkeeper of the Year. Banks won the FIFA Goalkeeper of the Year award six times, along with several other individual awards, and was an inaugural inductee into the English Football Hall of Fame in 2002.

4. Another English great was Peter Shilton, who currently holds the records for England caps with 125 and most competitive games in world soccer at 1,390. He made his Leicester debut as a 16-year-old and his arrival enabled the Foxes to sell Gordon Banks to Stoke City. Shilton even scored for the team in a 1967 match. The team was relegated after the next season but reached the FA Cup final. He won the Second Division title in 1970-71 and the 1971 FA Charity Shield. Shilton was 32 years old when he made his World Cup debut but posted 10 clean sheets in 17 tournament matches to share the record for World Cup clean sheets with Fabien Barthez. He joined Stoke in 1974, and later at Nottingham Forest, he won several trophies, including the First Division championship, two European Cups, a UEFA Super Cup, and a League Cup. Shilton also

won several individual honors and was inducted into the English Football Hall of Fame.

5. The Schmeichel name has long been associated with great goalkeeping, and Kasper is following in the footsteps of his famous father Peter. The Danish international currently ranks number one in clean sheets for the club, second in appearances for a keeper, and the 34-year-old was still playing with the Foxes as of April 2021. Kasper joined from Leeds United in June 2011 and helped the team win the 2013-14 Championship League and 2015-16 Premier League crowns. He has won several awards while with the Foxes, including the Danish Football Player of the Year in 2016 and 2017, the Football League Team of the Decade for 2005-2015, the PFA Championship Team of the Year for 2013-14, the Leicester Player of the Season and the Player's Player of the Season for 2011-12 and 2016-17, and the Leicester City Supporters' Club Player of the Season for 2011-12.

6. American international Kasey Keller arrived at Leicester in 1996 from Millwall and stayed for three years before joining Rayo Vallecano on a free transfer when his contract expired. In between, he played 125 games and posted 45 clean sheets. He was a superb shot-stopper as the number-one choice for manager Martin O'Neill. He appeared in 99 Premier League outings and helped the team win the 1996-97 League Cup final replay at Hillsborough. Keller was named the US Soccer

Federation's Player of the Year for 1997 and played for his homeland in the 1998 World Cup in France.

7. Ian Walker made a name for himself with Tottenham Hotspur while playing over 250 games for the London side. After a decade with Spurs, Walker handed management a transfer request in September 2000 and was transferred to Leicester for £2.5 million in July 2001. However, the team was relegated in his first season. He helped the club earn promotion back to the Premier League at the first attempt and was recalled to the English national team for the first time in six years. He struggled the following season and conceded 5 goals in 18 minutes against Aston Villa in January 2004, which led to a fan invading the pitch to confront him. The Foxes were soon relegated again, and Walker was released in 2005, after 44 clean sheets in 156 games.

8. George Hebden was a fearless and talented keeper who served in World War I as a teenager. He joined Leicester in May 1920 from Barking Town after impressing the club's scouts. He arrived as a backup but a year later took over from Herbert Bown as the number one. Hebden played 101 league games with the Foxes, and three in the FA Cup, with 39 clean sheets to his name. He left for Queens Park Rangers in May 1925 and later played for Gillingham.

9. Paul Henderson began his career in his Australian homeland before joining Bradford City in England in July

2004 and he joined Leicester on trial in May 2005. Henderson played 75 contests with the team over the next four years while posting 25 clean sheets. He originally signed as back up to Rab Douglas, but soon became the number one for manager Rob Kelly. However, when fellow keepers Ben Alnwick and Márton Fülöp were with the club, Henderson's playing time decreased and the team was relegated in 2008. He helped the side win the second-tier League One title in 2008-09 to return to the top tier but was released in May 2009 and returned to Australia to play.

10. After playing non-league football, Joe Calvert ended up with Bristol Rovers in 1931-32 and was then transferred to Leicester. He remained with the side during World War II before leaving in January 1948 for Watford, where he ended his career. Yorkshire-born Calvert was a former pit worker who was 24 before he sampled his first taste of senior football. Calvert was almost 41 years old when playing his last game with the Foxes, to become the club's oldest competitive player at the time. He played 80 official games with the side, with 18 clean sheets, and appeared in over 60 more unofficial outings during the war.

CHAPTER 5:

DARING DEFENDERS

QUIZ TIME!

1. Which player made the most all-time appearances for the club?
   a. Graham Cross
   b. Adam Black
   c. Steve Walsh
   d. John Sjoberg
2. Jimmy Willis was shown 10 yellow cards in the 1994-95 Premier League season.
   a. True
   b. False
3. Which player scored 4 goals in all competitions in 2019-20?
   a. Çağlar Söyüncü
   b. Ben Chilwell
   c. Jonny Evans
   d. Ricardo Pereira

4. How many goals did Matt Elliot tally in the 1999-00 domestic league season?
   a. 10
   b. 7
   c. 6
   d. 3
5. Which player posted 3 goals in the 2015-16 Premier League?
   a. Marcin Wasilewski
   b. Danny Simpson
   c. Ritchie De Laet
   d. Robert Huth
6. How many appearances did John Sjoberg make in all competitions for the Foxes?
   a. 362
   b. 387
   c. 414
   d. 435
7. Michael Morrison netted 6 goals in the 2008-09 League One campaign.
   a. True
   b. False
8. Which defender was named the club's Player of the Year for 2017-18?
   a. Wes Morgan
   b. Harry Maguire

c. Ricardo Pereira
d. Çağlar Söyüncü

9. Which player made 48 appearances in all competitions in 2016-17?

   a. Christian Fuchs
   b. Wes Morgan
   c. Danny Simpson
   d. Molla Wagué

10. How many goals did Wes Morgan score in the 2018-19 Premier League?

    a. 7
    b. 5
    c. 3
    d. 1

11. How many appearances did Adam Black make in all competitions with the Foxes?

    a. 452
    b. 466
    c. 531
    d. 557

12. In the 2003-04 Premier League season, a total of 5 Leicester defenders were shown red cards.

    a. True
    b. False

13. Steve Walsh joined the Foxes from which team?

a. Cardiff City FC
b. Bristol Rovers FC
c. Wigan Athletic
d. Norwich City FC

14. Which player received 18 caps from the Scottish men's national team while playing for Leicester?

a. John Sjoberg
b. Ian King
c. Matt Elliot
d. Billy Frame

15. Which player posted 4 goals in all competitions in 2009-10?

a. Ryan McGivern
b. Jack Hobbs
c. Michael Morrison
d. Bruno Berner

16. John Sjoberg played his entire pro career with the Foxes.

a. True
b. False

17. How many official appearances did Graham Cross make in all competitions for Leicester?

a. 523
b. 544
c. 578
d. 600

18. Steve Whitworth left Leicester to join which club?

    a. Sunderland AFC
    b. Tottenham Hotspur
    c. Middlesbrough FC
    d. Sheffield Wednesday FC

19. Which player made 44 appearances in all competitions in 2017-18?

    a. Christian Fuchs
    b. Harry Maguire
    c. Aleksandar Dragović
    d. Ben Chilwell

20. John O'Neill made 39 appearances for the Northern Irish men's football team while playing for Leicester.

    a. True
    b. False

QUIZ ANSWERS

1. A – Graham Cross
2. B – False
3. D – Ricardo Pereira
4. C – 6
5. D – Robert Huth
6. C – 414
7. B – False
8. B – Harry Maguire
9. A – Christian Fuchs
10. C – 3
11. D – 557
12. B – False
13. C – Wigan Athletic
14. C – Matt Elliot
15. D – Bruno Berner
16. B – False
17. D – 600
18. A – Sunderland AFC
19. B – Harry Maguire
20. A – True

DID YOU KNOW?

1. Leicester defenders who have been named the club's Player of the Year since 1987-88 are: 1987-88, Steve Walsh; 1988-89, Alan Paris; 1989-90, Gary Mills; 1990-91-Tony James; 1991-92, Gary Mills; 1992-93, Colin Hill; 1993-94, Simon Grayson; 1996-97, Simon Grayson; 1997-98, Matt Elliott; 1999-2000, Gerry Taggart; 2004-05, Danny Tiatto; 2007-08, Richard Stearman; 2009-10, Jack Hobbs; 2012-13, Wes Morgan; 2017-18, Harry Maguire; 2018-19, Ricardo Pereira.
2. William Henry "Harry" Bailey was one of the original club defenders. He played with Leicester Fosse from 1884 to 1899 and appeared in over 100 official games. Bailey was also an accomplished cricket player and was considered to be one of Victorian Leicester's sporting stars. The full-back played in the club's first games in the Midlands' League and the Football League, scored the team's first penalty, and became the first Leicester player to make 100 appearances. After hanging up his boots and cricket bat, Bailey ran the Full Moon Pub in Russell Square, Leicester.
3. Graham Cross began his pro career with hometown club Leicester from 1961 to 1975 and is currently ranked number one for all-time appearances with the squad at 600. He was quite versatile, he started as a forward and could also play in midfield. He helped the side reach the

FA Cup final in 1962-63 and 1968-69 and reached the League Cup final in 1963-64 and 1964-65, winning it in 1963-64. He also won the Second Division title in 1970-71 and the 1971 FA Charity Shield. Cross was also a fine cricket player with Leicestershire between 1961 and 1977. The Foxes loaned him to Chesterfield in 1975-76, and he joined Brighton and Hove Albion shortly after.

4. Ranked number two on the Foxes' appearance list at 557 is Adam Black of Scotland with 528 of those games coming in league action. He arrived at Filbert Street from Bathgate in 1920 and played until hanging up his boots in 1935. Black won the Distinguished Conduct Medal in World War I for his gallantry and then helped the team win the Second Division title in 1924-25 and finish as runners-up in the First Division in 1928-29. He also wore the captain's armband for a spell but managed just 4 goals with the side, with 3 of those coming on penalty kicks and the other being a free kick. There's a suite named in Black's honor at King Power Stadium.

5. Turkish international Çağlar Söyüncü began his career in his homeland before joining SC Freiburg of Germany's Bundesliga in 2016. He then joined Leicester in 2018 ,and is already considered by many to be one of the club's best defenders ever. After costing a reported £18 million transfer fee, he's been one of the side's steadiest and most skilled players. Söyüncü is a modern-day defender who possesses strong playmaking and dribbling abilities, while displaying aerial dominance. He was named to the

PFA Premier League Team of the Year for 2019-20 and, as of April 2021, was approaching his 75th appearance for the Foxes.

6. Like Wes Morgan, Frank Sinclair was an English-born defender who played internationally with Jamaica. He graduated through the Chelsea youth system before joining Leicester in 1998. He remained with the side until joining Burnley in 2002. Sinclair went on to play close to 800 club games in his 25-year career and won several team trophies with Chelsea. He also helped Leicester capture the 1999-2000 League Cup and earn promotion to the top tier in 2002-03. Sinclair played just under 200 games with the Foxes and turned to football management after hanging up his boots.

7. After playing in his homeland of Australia, Patrick Kisnorbo moved to Heart of Midlothian in Scotland in 2003 and was bought by Leicester in April 2005. Kisnorbo soon became a fan favorite during his four seasons with the club after moving from the midfield to defense. He was named the Players' Player of the Year for 2006-07, and chipped in with 12 goals in 140 games before leaving for Leeds United on a free transfer in 2009. The team was relegated to the third tier following the 2007-08 campaign and Kisnorbo helped it gain promotion back to the second tier in 2008-09 before leaving.

8. Northern Ireland international Gerry Taggart was named the club's Player of the Year for 1999-2000 after helping the

side win the League Cup. He arrived in 1998 from Bolton Wanderers and also helped the team finish runners-up in the League Cup in 1998-99 and in the second-tier Division One in 2002-03. Taggart, who played 51 times for his homeland, appeared in 142 games with the Foxes, and posted 12 goals. He joined Stoke City in December 2003 for two months and soon joined the club permanently. Taggart returned to Leicester in 2007 as a first-team coach and became a caretaker manager soon after. He then briefly became a radio pundit for Foxes games.

9. Simon Grayson joined the club from Leeds United in 1992, playing 229 matches before joining Aston Villa in 1997, chipping in with 6 goals. He was named the team's Player of the Year for 1993-94 and 1996-97. He was a dependable full-back in Division One and the Premier League and could also play in the midfield if needed. Grayson captained the side to its 1993-1994 playoff triumph against Derby County at Wembley to earn promotion to the top flight and helped it win the 1996-97 League Cup. He became a football manager after retiring from playing.

10. Austrian international Christian Fuchs arrived at King Power Stadium in June 2015 on a free transfer from Schalke 04 in Germany and helped the team top the Premier League in his first season. This made Fuchs the second Austrian to receive a Premier League winners' medal after Alex Manninger of Arsenal in 1998. Fuchs proved to be an excellent tackler and pass interceptor with the team and was still with the Foxes as of April

2021, as he turned down an offer to play in America and chose to remain in Leicester. He has now played over 150 games for the club and is still going strong.

CHAPTER 6:

MAESTROS OF THE MIDFIELD

QUIZ TIME!

1. Who made the most appearances in all competitions for the Foxes?
    a. John O'Neill
    b. Sep Smith
    c. Mal Griffiths
    d. Hughie Adcock
2. Sep Smith played his entire pro career with Leicester.
    a. True
    b. False
3. How many goals did Andy King score in all competitions in 2009-10?
    a. 5
    b. 8
    c. 11
    d. 15

4. Which player tallied 7 assists in the 2017-18 Premier League season?

    a. Vicente Iborra
    b. Marc Albrighton
    c. Adrien Silva
    d. Hamza Choudhury

5. Mal Griffiths left this club to join Leicester.

    a. Swansea City FC
    b. Arsenal FC
    c. Tottenham Hotspur
    d. Aston Villa

6. This player scored 8 goals in the 1999-00 Premier League season.

    a. Robbie Savage
    b. Stefan Oakes
    c. Muzzy Izzet
    d. Andy Impey

7. Marc Albrighton appeared in 47 matches in all competitions in 2016-17.

    a. True
    b. False

8. Which Scottish club did Danny Liddle leave to join the Foxes?

    a. St Mirren FC
    b. East Fife FC

c. Aberdeen FC
d. Motherwell FC

9. Who netted 8 goals in the team's first Premier League season?

    a. David Oldfield
    b. Mark Andrew Draper
    c. Mark Robins
    d. David Lowe

10. How many appearances did Sep Smith make for Leicester in all competitions?

    a. 384
    b. 373
    c. 368
    d. 340

11. Which player won the club's Player of the Year award in 2013-14.

    a. Danny Drinkwater
    b. Lloyd Dyer
    c. Anthony Knockaert
    d. Andy King

12. Andy King made 50 appearances for the Welsh men's national team while playing for Leicester.

    a. True
    b. False

13. Which club did Danny Drinkwater leave to join the Foxes?

    a. Preston North End
    b. Fulham FC
    c. Manchester United
    d. Liverpool FC

14. This player scored 5 goals in the 2014-15 Premier League season.

    a. Matty James
    b. Jeffrey Schlupp
    c. Andy King
    d. Esteban Cambiasso

15. How many appearances did John O'Neill make in all competitions with the Foxes?

    a. 345
    b. 322
    c. 287
    d. 263

16. Youri Tielemans was the only Leicester player to be shown a red card in the 2019-20 domestic league season.

    a. True
    b. False

17. Who contributed 8 goals in the 2004-05 Championship League?

    a. Andy Welsh
    b. Gareth Williams

c. Joey Guðjónsson
d. Stephen Hughes

18. How many assists did Lloyd Dyer record in the 2017-18 domestic league?
    a. 3
    b. 6
    c. 8
    d. 13

19. How many appearances did Hughie Adcock make in all competitions with Leicester?
    a. 479
    b. 528
    c. 460
    d. 593

20. Stephen Hughes appeared in every game in the 2006-07 domestic league season.
    a. True
    b. False

QUIZ ANSWERS

1. D – Hughie Adcock
2. A – True
3. C – 11
4. B – Marc Albrighton
5. B – Arsenal FC
6. C – Muzzy Izzet
7. A – True
8. B – East Fife FC
9. D – David Lowe
10. B – 373
11. A – Danny Drinkwater
12. A – True
13. C – Manchester United
14. D – Esteban Cambiasso
15. A – 345
16. B – False
17. C – Joey Guðjónsson
18. D – 8
19. C – 460
20. B – False

DID YOU KNOW?

1. Leicester midfielders who have been named the club's Player of the Year since 1987-88 are: 1995-96, Garry Parker; 2000-01, Robbie Savage; 2001-02, Robbie Savage; 2005-06, Joey Guðjónsson; 2010-11, Richie Wellens; 2013-14, Danny Drinkwater; and 2014-15, Esteban Cambiasso.
2. French international N'Golo Kanté was a key player for the Foxes in 2015-16 when they unexpectedly won the Premier League. He joined from Caen in August 2015 and spent just one season with the club, being named to the PFA Premier League Team of the Year, as well as Leicester's Players' Player of the Year. Kanté led the league with 157 interceptions and 175 tackles that campaign before being sold to Chelsea for £32.22 million. He won the Premier League again the next season with Chelsea and was named the PFA Players' Player of the Year, the FWA Footballer of the Year, the Premier League Player of the Season, and Chelsea Players' Player of the Year.
3. A Leicester legend, Mustafa Kemal "Muzzy" Izzet was an English-born Turkish international who played 319 games for the club and scored 47 goals. He helped the side win the League Cup in 1996-97 and 1999-2000 while winning a runners-up medal in 1998-99. He also won the First Division playoffs with the team in 1995-96 and a First Division runners-up medal for 2002-03. Izzet was

initially signed on loan by the Foxes in March 1996, and he signed permanently a few months later. He then left for Birmingham City in June 2004, following Leicester's relegation.

4. Northern Ireland international Neil Lennon was well known as the manager of several clubs, including Glasgow Celtic until February 2021, but most Foxes' fans will remember him as one of Leicester's elite midfielders. He arrived from Crewe Alexandra in February 1996 for a reported £750,000, won the League Cup in 1996-97 and 1999-2000, as well as the First Division playoffs in 1995-96. Lennon was rejected as a youngster by Manchester City, and then missed nearly a year of action with a back injury, before arriving at Filbert Street. He formed an effective partnership with Muzzy Izzet. After 208 matches, Lennon joined Celtic in 2000 for a reported of £5.75 million and won several trophies with the club.

5. Danny Drinkwater was a popular box-to-box midfielder who arrived at Leicester from Manchester United in January 2012. He helped the side capture the 2013-14 Championship League and the 2015-16 Premier League, while being named to the PFA Championship League Team of the Year for 2013-14. In fact, he also won the 2013-14 Leicester Player of the Season and Goal of the Season awards. He signed a new five-year contract in August 2016 but was sold for £34.11 million to Chelsea a year later, after 218 games with the Foxes. Drinkwater has

basically been out on loan to various clubs since joining Chelsea and was playing in Turkey in 2020-21.

6. Argentine international Esteban Cambiasso left Inter Milan in August 2014 to join Leicester just after the club was promoted back to the Premier League for winning the 2013-14 Championship League. He signed a one-year deal on a free transfer and was so impressive that he was named the club's Player of the Year. Cambiasso chipped in with 5 goals in his 33 appearances, but disappointed Foxes' supporters by turning down a new contract offer in 2015 and joining Olympiacos in Greece. The underrated midfielder won over 20 team trophies as well as several individual awards.

7. Controversial Welsh international Robbie Savage was acquired by Leicester for a reported £400,000 from Crewe Alexandra in July 1997, after spending his youth career with Manchester United. He played just over 200 games, and contributed 9 goals, before the club was relegated from the Premier League at the end of the 2001-02 campaign. Savage then joined newly promoted Birmingham City for a reported fee of £1.25 million. He helped the Foxes reach the League Cup final in 1998-99 and win it the next season. He was named the club's Player of the Year in 2000-01 and 2001-02. Savage is currently a well-known media pundit in the UK.

8. The first decade of Northern Ireland international John O'Neill's career was spent with Leicester from 1977 to

1987 before departing for Queens Park Rangers. He played 345 times for the Foxes and scored 12 goals. He joined Norwich City shortly after leaving QPR but, after 34 minutes of his first game with Norwich, he was on the receiving end of a brutal tackle by John Fashanu of Wimbledon. O'Neill's knee ligaments were badly torn, and he never played another pro game. O'Neill began legal proceedings against Fashanu and later settled the case out of court for a reported £70,000.

9. After spending his youth career with Manchester United, Richie Wellens went on to play with several clubs during his pro career, including a stint with Leicester from 2009 to 2013. He arrived from Doncaster Rovers and netted 6 goals in 147 contests. Wellens was named the Foxes Player of the Year for 2010-11 and wore the captain's armband for several games in 2011-12. However, his season came to an early end after he suffered a knee injury. He was then loaned to Ipswich Town for a month and in July 2013 Wellens returned to Doncaster. He later became a football manager.

10. Scottish international Ian Wilson spent his youth career in his homeland but didn't make his pro debut until joining Leicester in 1979 for a reported £20,000. He captained the team for part of his stint at Filbert Street and helped the side win the 1979-80 Second Division crown. Wilson joined Everton in September 1987 for a reported £300,000 after making 318 appearances and notching 19 goals with the Foxes. He later played with Beşiktaş and won the

Turkish League Championship and Turkish Cup before operating soccer schools after hanging up his boots.

CHAPTER 7:

SENSATIONAL STRIKERS/FORWARDS

QUIZ TIME!

1. Who played more career matches with the Foxes?
   a. Arthur Chandler
   b. Mike Stringfellow
   c. Arthur Rowley
   d. Derek Hines
2. Riyad Mahrez tallied 13 assists in the 2015-16 Premier League.
   a. True
   b. False
3. Which club did Jamie Vardy join Leicester from?
   a. Fleetwood Town FC
   b. AFC Bournemouth
   c. Luton Town FC
   d. Millwall FC

4. Which player appeared in 37 games in the Foxes' first Premier League season?

    a. Julian Joachim
    b. Mark Robins
    c. Iwan Roberts
    d. Jamie Lawrence

5. How many goals did Steve Howard score in the 2008-09 domestic league season?

    a. 7
    b. 18
    c. 9
    d. 13

6. How many appearances did Derek Hines make in all competitions with Leicester?

    a. 360
    b. 332
    c. 317
    d. 275

7. Arthur Chandler spent his whole career with the Foxes.

    a. True
    b. False

8. Which played scored 16 goals in all competitions in 2016-17?

    a. Riyad Mahrez
    b. Islam Slimani

c. Jamie Vardy
d. Shinji Okazaki

9. How many goals did Yakubu Aiyegbeni score in the 2010-11 Championship League?

a. 5
b. 14
c. 7
d. 11

10. Which player netted 9 goals in the 2012-13 domestic league?

a. Chris Wood
b. Jamie Vardy
c. Harry Kane
d. Martyn Waghorn

11. How many appearances did Mike Stringfellow make in all competitions with the Foxes?

a. 396
b. 370
c. 355
d. 317

12. Emile Heskey played in every domestic league game in the 1997-98 season.

a. True
b. False

13. Which club did David Nugent leave to join Leicester?

a. Preston North End
b. Tranmere Rovers FC
c. West Ham United
d. Portsmouth FC

14. How many goals did Ayoze Pérez score in the 2019-20 Premier League season?

a. 13
b. 11
c. 8
d. 5

15. Who won the 2015-16 PFA Players' Player of the Year award?

a. Shinji Okazaki
b. Leonardo Ulloa
c. Joe Dodoo
d. Riyad Mahrez

16. Chris Wood was shown 7 yellow cards in all competitions in 2012-13.

a. True
b. False

17. How many appearances did Arthur Chandler make in all appearances with Leicester?

a. 322
b. 346
c. 419
d. 468

18. Which player scored 13 goals in the 2002-03 domestic league season?

    a. Tommy Wright
    b. James Scowcroft
    c. Brian Deane
    d. Trevor Benjamin

19. Tony Cottee was acquired by Leicester from this outfit.

    a. Selangor FC
    b. Newcastle United
    c. Burnley FC
    d. Norwich City FC

20. Iain Hume scored only 12 goals in all competitions with Leicester.

    a. True
    b. False

QUIZ ANSWERS

1. A – Arthur Chandler
2. B – False
3. A – Fleetwood Town FC
4. C – Iwan Roberts
5. D – 13
6. C – 317
7. B – False
8. C – Jamie Vardy
9. D – 11
10. A – Chris Wood
11. B – 370
12. B – False
13. D – Portsmouth FC
14. C – 8
15. D – Riyad Mahrez
16. B – False
17. C – 419
18. C – Brian Deane
19. A – Selangor FC
20. B – False

DID YOU KNOW?

1. Leicester forwards who have been honored with the club's Player of the Year Award since 1987-88 are: 1998-99, Tony Cottee; 2002-03, Paul Dickov; 2003-04, Les Ferdinand; 2006-07, Iain Hume; 2008-09, Steve Howard; 2015-16, Riyad Mahrez; and 2019-20, Jamie Vardy.
2. With 460 games under his belt for the Foxes, Hugh "Hughie" Adcock shares third place on the club's all-time appearance list with goalkeeper Mark Wallington. The outside-right also chipped in with 52 goals between 1923 and 1935 after arriving from the nearby Loughborough Corinthians and before leaving for Bristol Rovers. The English international helped the side capture the Second Division title in 1924-25 and finish as First Division runners-up in 1928-29.
3. Welsh international outside-right William Maldwyn "Mal" Griffiths was picked up from Arsenal in 1938 and remained with the club for an 18-year stint, until joining Burton Albion in 1956. He appeared in 409 official games, scoring 76 goals, and he also played several unofficial contests during World War II. While the Foxes won the Second Division title the season before Griffiths arrived, and again the season after he left, he did help the squad hoist the crown in 1953-54. He currently stands at number nine on the club's all-time appearance list.

4. Japanese international Shinji Okazaki helped the Foxes capture the Premier League title after arriving from German club Mainz in June 2015 for a reported £7 million fee. Okazaki scored several important goals during that historic season and became just the second Japanese player to win the Premier League after Shinji Kagawa at Manchester United. His performances that historic season also saw him win the Asian International Player of the Year Award. Okazaki tallied 19 goals in 137 outings before being released in 2019. He was playing with Huesca in Spain in 2020-21 and has scored 50 times in 119 outings for Japan.

5. Len Glover joined the Foxes from Charlton Athletic in November 1967 for what was then a record English fee of £80,000 for a winger. He was a fan favorite who went on to play in 306 official games while contributing 48 goals. He helped the side reach the 1968-69 FA Cup final and win the Second Division title in 1970-71 along with the 1971 FA Charity Shield. Glover joined Kettering Town in 1976 and later captained the Tampa Bay Rowdies in America.

6. Although Allan Clarke's career with the Foxes lasted just 46 games and 16 goals in 1968-69, the English international made the headlines several times. He arrived from Fulham for what was then a record British transfer fee of £150,000 and then joined Leeds United a year later for another record fee of £165,000. He scored some important goals for the club including a hat trick against Manchester City and

the winner in the FA Cup semi-final tilt against West Bromwich Albion. With Leeds, Clarke won an FA Cup, First Division title, FA Charity Shield, Inter-Cities Fairs Cup, and several runners-up medals. He later became a well-known manager.

7. Steve Claridge scored 21 times in 79 outings with Leicester and had a knack for netting important goals. He was 29 years old when arriving from Birmingham City in March 1996 and struggled early on. However, he scored the last-minute extra-time winner in the 1996 First Division playoffs, against Crystal Palace to earn the Foxes promotion to the Premier League. Claridge followed up the next season with the extra-time winner in the League Cup final against Middlesbrough, which saw Leicester qualify for Europe. In 1998, he was loaned to Portsmouth and then joined Wolverhampton Wanderers. Remarkably, Claridge played for over 20 clubs during his career from 1983 to 2017 before becoming a football manager.

8. Don Revie became famous as the manager of Leeds United and England, but he should also be remembered for tallying 29 goals for Leicester in 110 official appearances and he also played several more games during World War II. The English international center-forward began his career with the Foxes in August 1944 when he was an apprentice bricklayer and made his debut in 1946 after the war. He helped the team reach the 1948-49 FA Cup final but missed the game due to injury. He was then sold to Hull City for a reported £19,000 in

November 1949. Revie would later be named the FWA Footballer of the Year for 1954-55 while playing with Manchester City and won several trophies as Leeds's manager.

9. Scottish international Paul Dickov arrived at Filbert Street from Manchester City in 2002 but the club was relegated following the 2002-03 season. Dickov tallied a career-best 20 goals in 2002-03 to help the side earn promotion back to the Premier League by finishing as First Division runners-up and he was named the club's Player of the Year. He scored another 13 goals in 2003-04 but the team was once again relegated, and he joined Blackburn Rovers after turning down a contract offer from the Foxes. Dickov rejoined Leicester in August 2008 and helped the side win the third-tier League One championship. He joined Derby County on loan in August 2009 and was released by Leicester in February 2010 after scoring 40 goals in 125 appearances.

10. Another favorite with Foxes' fans was Scottish-born Canadian international Iain Hume, who arrived from Tranmere Rovers in August 2005 for a reported £500,000. He had pace to burn and played with plenty of passion, which led to him being named the club's Player of the Year for 2006-07. He won the team's Goal of the Year Award in 2007-08 but the squad was relegated following the campaign. Hume then joined Barnsley for a reported £1.2 million fee after scoring 34 goals for the club in 132 outings. He later played in India and Spain.

CHAPTER 8:

NOTABLE TRANSFERS/SIGNINGS

QUIZ TIME!

1. Who was the club's most expensive signing?
   a. Wesley Fofana
   b. Ayoze Pérez
   c. Islam Slimani
   d. Youri Tielemans
2. Midfielder Danny Drinkwater was sold to Arsenal in 2017-18.
   a. True
   b. False
3. Which player was sold for Leicester's record transfer fee?
   a. Riyad Mahrez
   b. Harry Maguire
   c. Danny Drinkwater
   d. Ben Chilwell
4. Who was the club's most expensive signing in 2017-18?

a. Kelechi Iheanacho
b. Adrien Silva
c. Vicente Iborra
d. Islam Slimani

5. What was the transfer fee Leicester paid to sign Ayoze Pérez?

   a. £15 million
   b. £27 million
   c. £30.06 million
   d. £36 million

6. Which club did Leicester sign Islam Slimani from?

   a. Eintracht Frankfurt
   b. Valencia FC
   c. SM Caen
   d. Sporting CP

7. Leicester sold Riyad Mahrez to the Spanish club Real Madrid.

   a. True
   b. False

8. Which team was Harry Maguire sold to?

   a. Manchester United
   b. Paris Saint-Germain
   c. Juventus
   d. Liverpool FC

9. How much did the Foxes pay to acquire Wesley Fofana?

a. €26 million
b. €31.5 million
c. €35 million
d. €40 million

10. Which player was acquired from Coventry City in June 2018?

a. James Maddison
b. Ricardo Pereira
c. Filip Benković
d. Çağlar Söyüncü

11. What was the transfer fee the Foxes received for Danny Drinkwater?

a. £36 million
b. £38 million
c. £41 million
d. £34.11 million

12. The Foxes did not make an official signing in 2005-06.

a. True
b. False

13. Leicester signed Youri Tielemans from which side?

a. FC Lille
b. OGC Nice
c. FC Girondins de Bordeaux
d. AS Monaco

14. Which player was the most expensive departure in 2016-17?

a. Chris Wood
b. David Nugent
c. N'Golo Kanté
d. Jeffrey Schlupp

15. What was the transfer fee Leicester paid to sign Youri Tielemans?

    a. £52 million
    b. £40.5 million
    c. £36 million
    d. £30 million

16. The club sold Harry Maguire for a transfer fee of £78.3 million.

    a. True
    b. False

17. Which club did Leicester sign Ayoze Pérez from?

    a. Newcastle United
    b. CD Tenerife
    c. West Bromwich Albion
    d. RCD Espanyol

18. What was the transfer fee Leicester received for Riyad Mahrez?

    a. £50 million
    b. £57 million
    c. £61.02 million
    d. £68 million

19. Ben Chilwell was sent to which side in 2020-21?

    a. Peterborough United
    b. Reading FC
    c. Wigan Athletic
    d. Chelsea FC

20. Leicester signed four players from Manchester United in 2012-13.

    a. True
    b. False

QUIZ ANSWERS

1. D – Youri Tielemans
2. B – False
3. B – Harry Maguire
4. A – Kelechi Iheanacho
5. C – £30.06 million
6. D – Sporting CP
7. B – False
8. A – Manchester United
9. C – £31.5 million
10. A – James Maddison
11. D – £45.18 million
12. B – False
13. D – As Monaco
14. C – N'Golo Kanté
15. B – £40.5 million
16. A – True
17. A – Newcastle United
18. C – £61.02
19. D – Hull City FC
20. B – False

DID YOU KNOW?

1. The top five transfer fees paid by Leicester as of April 2021 are: midfielder Youri Tielemans from AS Monaco for £40.5 million in 2019-20; defender Wesley Fofana from Saint-Étienne for £31.5 million in 2020-21; forward Ayoze Pérez from Newcastle United for £30.06 million in 2019-20; forward Islam Slimani from Sporting CP for £27.9 million in 2016-17; and forward Kelechi Iheanacho from Manchester City for £24.93 million in 2017-18.

2. The top five transfer fees received by the Foxes as of April 2021 are: defender Harry Maguire to Manchester United for £78.3 million in 2019-20; winger Riyad Mahrez to Manchester City for £61.02 million in 2018-19; defender Ben Chilwell to Chelsea FC for £45.18 million in 2020-21; midfielder Danny Drinkwater to Chelsea FC for £34.11 million in 2017-18; midfielder N'Golo Kanté to Chelsea FC for £32.22 million in 2016-17.

3. Belgian international midfielder Youri Tielemans kicked off his pro career with Anderlecht in 2013 and notched 35 goals in 185 official appearances. He helped the side win the league title twice, was named the Belgian Young Professional Footballer of the Year for 2013-14 and 2014-15, and Belgian Professional Footballer of the Year for 2016-17. Tielemans joined Monaco for £23.58 million in July 2017 but was loaned to Leicester in January 2019. He

was bought for a club-record £40.5 million six months later. Tielemans was about to reach the 100-game mark for the Foxes in April 2021 and had scored 16 goals.

4. French center-back Wesley Fofana cost the club £31.5 million when purchased from Saint-Étienne in October 2020, and then promptly signed a five-year contract. Fofana had made his debut with the French club in May 2019 at the age of 19 and played just 30 games with the side, scoring 2 goals, before joining Leicester. As of April 1, 2021, the youngster had appeared in 27 contests with the Foxes and had yet to score a goal.

5. Attacking midfielder/forward Ayoze Pérez began his career at hometown club CD Tenerife and won several individual awards with the Segunda División club in 2013-14. He joined Newcastle United for £1.8 million in June 2014 after reportedly turning down Real Madrid, Barcelona, and Porto. He then joined Leicester in July 2019 for £30.06 million. He tallied 8 goals in 40 games in 2019-20 and had 3 more in his first 26 matches of 2020-21. Pérez's brother Samuel currently plays for Alnwick Town in the Northern Football Alliance Premier Division, and his cousin María José Pérez plays for the Spanish women's national team.

6. Algerian international striker Islam Slimani joined the Foxes from Sporting Lisbon on the last day of the 2016-17 summer transfer window for what was then a club-record £27.9 million. After scoring 13 goals in 47 games, Slimani

was sent to Newcastle United in January 2018 until the end of the season. He played just four games and was sent to Turkish Süper Lig club Fenerbahçe in August 2018 on a season-long loan, and scored 5 goals in 25 outings. The next season saw him play on loan with Monaco, where he notched 9 goals in 19 games. Slimani played once for Leicester in 2020-21 before joining Olympique Lyonnais on a free transfer in January 2021.

7. After playing with Manchester City from 2015 to 2017, scoring 21 goals in 64 games and helping them win the 2015-16 League Cup, forward Kelechi Ịheanachọ joined Leicester for £24.93 million in August 2017. The Nigerian international became the first player in English football to be awarded a goal by VAR in January 2018 when he had incorrectly been ruled offside by on-pitch officials. He scored twice in the Foxes' 3-1 win over Manchester United in the quarterfinals of the FA Cup in March 2020-21 to send the team to the semi-finals for the first time since 1981-82. As of April 1, 2021, Iheanacho had scored 32 goals in 117 career games with Leicester.

8. Leicester's biggest transfer sale was the £78.3 million received for English international defender Harry Maguire from Manchester United in June 2017. He graduated through the youth system with Sheffield United and played over 150 times for the club while being named its Player of the Year for three consecutive seasons and to the PFA League One Team of the Year three times. Maguire joined Hull City for £2.84 million in 2014 and he

was named the Fans' Player of the Year and the Hull City Players' Player of the Year for 2016-17. He joined Leicester for £12.33 million in 2017 and was named the Player of the Season and the Players' Player of the Season for 2017-18 before being sold to Man United for a world-record fee for a defender. Maguire played 76 times for the Foxes and contributed 5 goals.

9. After scoring 48 goals in 179 games with Leicester and helping the side win the 2013-14 second-tier Championship League title, and the 2015-16 Premier League crown, Algerian international winger Riyad Mahrez was sold to Manchester City for £61.02 million in July 2018. He was also named to the PFA Premier League Team of the Year for 2015-16 and won the PFA Players' Player of the Year, the PFA Fans' Player of the Year, and the Leicester Player of the Year that season. Mahrez originally joined from Ac Le Havre in January 2014 for just £450,000.

10. Leicester made several big-money transfers with Chelsea between 2016-17 and 2020-21 as defender Ben Chilwell was sold to the London side for £45.18 million in August 2020, midfielder Danny Drinkwater went for £34.11 million in August 2017 and midfielder N'Golo Kanté was transferred for £32.22 in July 2016. Chilwell had come through the Foxes youth system while Drinkwater was bought from Manchester United for £810,000 in January 2012 and Kanté was bought from SM Caen in August 2015 for £8.10 million.

CHAPTER 9:

ODDS & ENDS

QUIZ TIME!

1. The Foxes' biggest domestic league defeat was 12-0 to what club in 1909?
    a. Leeds United
    b. Wolverhampton Wanderers
    c. Nottingham Forest
    d. Birmingham City FC
2. Leicester was given the nickname the Unbelievables after winning the 2015-16 Premier League.
    a. True
    b. False
3. Who was the youngest player to make an appearance for Leicester, at 15 years and 203 days old?
    a. Tomi Petrescu
    b. Joe Mattock
    c. Peter Shilton
    d. Ashley Chambers

4. What is the most games the Foxes have won in a domestic league season?

    a. 21
    b. 30
    c. 27
    d. 32

5. Which player scored the club's fastest hat trick in approximately 5 minutes?

    a. Arthur Chandler
    b. Fred Shinton
    c. Alan Smith
    d. Andy King

6. Which year was the Leicester City Women Football Club originally formed as an independent side?

    a. 1992
    b. 1998
    c. 2004
    d. 2006

7. Sep Smith played for Leicester for 12 years.

    a. True
    b. False

8. Leicester's biggest league victory was 10-1 over what club?

    a. Portsmouth FC
    b. Aston Villa

c. Tottenham Hotspur
d. Fulham FC

9. Who is the Foxes' oldest goal-scorer?

a. Dion Dublin
b. Paul Dickov
c. Les Ferdinand
d. Kevin Phillips

10. How many points did the Foxes record when they won the 2015-16 Premier League title?

a. 75
b. 78
c. 81
d. 93

11. The club's highest-scoring draw of 6-6 came against which side?

a. Club Brugge KV
b. Atlético Madrid
c. West Ham United
d. Arsenal FC

12. The first club Leicester hosted at King Power Stadium was Athletic Bilbao.

a. True
b. False

13. As of 2020, which player holds the club record for the fastest goal at 9 seconds?

a. Matty Fryatt
b. Arthur Rowley
c. Steve Walsh
d. Riyad Mahrez

14. What is the most domestic league defeats Leicester has suffered in a season?

a. 17
b. 21
c. 25
d. 28

15. Who is the oldest player to make an appearance for the Foxes at 43 years and 21 days old?

a. Kevin Phillips
b. Mark Schwarzer
c. Chris Powell
d. Martin Keown

16. The most draws Leicester posted in one domestic league season is 17.

a. True
b. False

17. The team's biggest victory in all competitions was 13-0 over what side?

a. Bradford City FC
b. Sunderland AFC
c. Manchester City
d. Notts Olympic FC

18. What is the most points the Foxes have recorded in a domestic league season?

    a. 107
    b. 102
    c. 96
    d. 90

19. Leicester's biggest victory in the Premier League as of 2020 was 9-0 against what outfit?

    a. Queens Park Rangers
    b. Stoke City FC
    c. Southampton FC
    d. Chelsea FC

20. The Foxes went on a club-record 9-game winning streak in the 2013-14 domestic league.

    a. True
    b. False

QUIZ ANSWERS

1. C – Nottingham Forest
2. A – True
3. D – Ashley Chambers
4. D – 32
5. B – Fred Shinton
6. C – 2004
7. B – False
8. A – Portsmouth FC
9. D – Kevin Phillips
10. C – 81
11. D – Arsenal FC
12. A – True
13. A – Matty Fryatt
14. C – 25
15. B – Mark Schwarzer
16. B – False
17. D – Notts Olympic FC
18. B – 102
19. C – Southampton FC
20. A – True

DID YOU KNOW?

1. The club entered a period of administration in October 2002 but was promoted back to the Premier League in 2003 and relegated again in 2004. Leicester City was then bought by Milan Mandarić in 2007 and relegated to the third tier of English soccer for the first time in club history in 2007-08. However, the side was promoted back to the second-tier Championship League the next season after winning the League 1 title in 2008-09.

2. In 2010, the club was taken over by a Thai-led group, Asian Football Investments, which was led by King Power's Khun Vichai Srivaddhanaprabha, who became chairman in 2011. His son, Khun Aiyawatt Srivaddhanaprabha, was one of two vice-chairmen. The King Power International Group is a travel retail company based in Bangkok and was owned by Khun Vichai Srivaddhanaprabha. He was succeeded as Leicester City's chairman by his son Khun Aiyawatt after Khun Vichai was sadly killed in a helicopter accident on Oct. 27, 2018, with four other people outside of King Power Stadium after taking off from the pitch.

3. King Power Stadium is also known as Filbert Way or Leicester City Stadium due to UEFA sponsorship regulations and was formerly known as the Walkers Stadium until 2011. The team moved in in 2002 with the

all-seater venue having a capacity of 32,261, making it currently the 20th largest soccer stadium in England.

4. The first game hosted at Leicester's new stadium was a 1-1 friendly draw with Athletic Bilbao of Spain. Bilbao's Tiko was the first player to score, and Jordan Stewart was the first Leicester player to find the back of the net. The first competitive outing at the venue was a 2-0 win over Watford.

5. The Filbert Street Stadium was officially named the City Business Stadium. It hosted Leicester's home games from 1891 to 2002 and was demolished in 2003. The record attendance at the ground was 47,298 for a fifth-round FA Cup match against Tottenham Hotspur on Feb. 18, 1928.

6. The club first included the image of a fox on its crest in 1948 because Leicestershire is well known for foxes and fox hunting. The team's mascot is a character named "Filbert Fox" and there are also secondary mascot characters known as "Cousin Dennis" and "Vickie Vixen."

7. A few years before World War II, Leicester started to play the "Post Horn Gallop" over the stadium's PA system before home games as the players came out of the tunnel. The club has since replaced the song with a modern version that is played as the players enter the pitch for the second half of a game. The club's motto, "Foxes Never Quit," is placed above the stadium's tunnel entrance.

8. The Leicester City Women Football Club is also nicknamed the Foxes and is based in Quorn, Leicestershire. The club

was formed independently in 2004 and was acquired by King Power in 2020. The team was competing in the FA Women's Championship in 2020-21, which is the second tier of English women's soccer. The side's home games are held at Farley Way Stadium with a capacity of 1,400.

9. The following Leicester players have been inducted into the English Football Hall of Fame: goalkeeper Gordon Banks of England as an inaugural inductee in 2002; goalkeeper Peter Shilton of England as an inaugural inductee in 2002; striker Gary Lineker of England in 2003; manager Don Revie of England in 2004; and midfielder Frank McLintock of Scotland in 2009.

10. The player with the longest recorded stint with the club was forward Sep Smith at 19 years and 249 days from Aug. 31, 1929, to May 7, 1949. The youngest first-team player was forward Ashley Chambers, at 15 years and 203 days when he played against Blackpool on Sept. 15, 2005. The oldest first-team player was goalkeeper Mark Schwarzer at 43 years and 21 days, against Hull City on Oct. 27, 2015.

CHAPTER 10:

DOMESTIC COMPETITION

QUIZ TIME!

1. How many combined league titles have the Foxes won at all levels of domestic competition?
   a. 5
   b. 9
   c. 13
   d. 15
2. Leicester has shared the FA Community Shield honors twice.
   a. True
   b. False
3. Which club did Leicester defeat to win its first League Cup?
   a. Liverpool FC
   b. Stoke City FC
   c. Manchester City
   d. Birmingham City FC

4. Which player scored the game-winner in the 1999-2000 League Cup final?
   a. Matt Elliot
   b. Tony Cottee
   c. Andy Impey
   d. Stefan Oakes
5. How many times has Leicester won the second-tier Second Division/Championship League?
   a. 4
   b. 7
   c. 3
   d. 10
6. Which side did the Foxes face in their first FA Cup final appearance?
   a. Manchester United
   b. Preston North End
   c. Brentford FC
   d. Wolverhampton Wanderers
7. The Foxes won their first Second Division/Championship League title in 1924-25.
   a. True
   b. False
8. How many times has the club won the League Cup?
   a. 6
   b. 5

c. 3
d. 1

9. Which team did the Foxes down to win the 1999-2000 League Cup final?
   a. Middlesbrough FC
   b. Bolton Wanderers
   c. Tranmere Rovers
   d. Aston Villa
10. Which two players are tied for most goals scored in FA Cup matches with 14 each?
    a. Mal Griffiths and Ernie Hine
    b. Arthur Chandler and Arthur Rowley
    c. Mike Stringfellow and Mal Griffiths
    d. Arthur Rowley and Johnny Duncan
11. Which club defeated Leicester in the 1968-69 FA Cup final?
    a. Manchester City FC
    b. Everton FC
    c. West Bromwich Albion
    d. Aston Villa
12. Leicester reached the semi-finals in their first year competing for the FA Cup.
    a. True
    b. False
13. How many times has the club finished as runners-up for the FA Cup?

a. 2
b. 4
c. 6
d. 8

14. Which squad did the Foxes face in the 2016 FA Community Shield?

a. Chelsea FC
b. Liverpool FC
c. Tottenham Hotspur
d. Manchester United

15. Who scored the game-winner in the 1971 FA Community Shield?

a. Stephen Whitworth
b. Alistair Brown
c. Malcolm Partridge
d. Graham Cross

16. Leicester has won the second-tier playoffs twice.

a. True
b. False

17. The Foxes finished as runners-up in the top-tier First Division for the first time in what season?

a. 1965-66
b. 1950-51
c. 1928-29
d. 1922-23

18. The club met which team in the 1998-99 League Cup final?

    a. Chelsea FC
    b. Tottenham Hotspur
    c. Queens Park Rangers
    d. Fulham FC

19. Which season did Leicester top the third-tier League One?

    a. 1955-56
    b. 1969-70
    c. 1980-81
    d. 2008-09

20. The Foxes competed in the English Wartime League and Cup competitions during World War II.

    a. True
    b. False

QUIZ ANSWERS

1. B – 9
2. B – False
3. B – Stoke City FC
4. A – Matt Elliot
5. B – 7
6. D – Wolverhampton Wanderers
7. A – True
8. C – 3
9. C – Tranmere Rovers
10. B – Arthur Chandler and Arthur Rowley
11. A – Manchester City FC
12. B – False
13. B – 4
14. D – Manchester United
15. A – Stephen Whitworth
16. A – True
17. C – 1928-29
18. B – Tottenham Hotspur
19. D – 2008-09
20. A – True

DID YOU KNOW?

1. On Oct. 25, 2019, the Foxes set the record for the highest margin in an away victory in the English top flight by hammering Southampton 9-0 at St Mary's Stadium. The result also tied the record for the highest margin of victory in the Premier League. Manchester United thumped Ipswich Town 9-0 at home in 1995 and also drilled Southampton 9-0 at home on Feb. 2, 2021.

2. Leicester's main domestic rivalries are with Nottingham Forest, Derby County, and Leicester City, since all four clubs are considered to play a "Midlands Derby" when they meet each other. However, the four clubs often play in different divisions of the four-tier English soccer pyramid, which means they typically meet if they're drawn against each other during the FA Cup or League Cup competitions.

3. The Toffees also have a rivalry with nearby Coventry City, which is just 24 miles away by automobile. This is known as the "M69 Derby" because the M69 motorway connects the city of Leicester with Coventry. These two clubs also currently play in different divisions, which means they usually only meet in domestic cup tournaments.

4. Leicester has won the top-tier First Division/Premier League title once and the second-tier Second Division/ First Division/Championship Division a record seven

times. The club has also captured the English League Cup three times and reached four FA Cup finals and won the third-tier League One once. They have also won the FA Charity/Community Shield once.

5. Leicester has been relegated 12 times. They were relegated from the top-tier First Division to the Second Division after the 1908-09, 1934-35, 1938-39, 1954-55, 1968-69, 1977-78, 1980-81, and 1986-87 campaigns. They were relegated from the top-tier Premier League to the second-tier Division One after 1994-95, 2001-02, and 2003-04. They were also relegated from the second-tier Championship League to the third-tier League One following the 2007-08 campaign.

6. The club's crowning achievement was to hoist the Premier League title in 2015-16 under manager Claudio Ranieri despite beginning the season as approximately 5000-1 underdogs. Leicester also came within a point of winning the 1928-29 First Division crown when they finished with 51 points to Sheffield Wednesday's 53 points.

7. The Foxes captured the second-tier Second Division/ First Division/ Championship League title in 1924-25, 1936-37, 1953-54, 1956-57, 1970-71, 1979-80, and 2013-14. They finished as runners-up in 1907-08 and 2002-03 and gained promotion to the top tier by winning the league playoffs in 1993-94 and 1995-96. The side topped the third-tier League One in 2008-09.

8. The squad's League Cup triumphs were celebrated in 1963-64, 1996-97, and 1999-2000 and they finished as runners-up in 1964-65 and 1998-99. They won the FA Charity Shield/Community Shield in 1971 and were runners-up in 2016. The team's four FA Cup appearances and defeats came in 1948-49, 1960-61, 1962-63, and 1968-69.
9. The English Wartime League was a soccer league competition that was held during World War II when the English Football League was suspended due to the conflict. The first season was held in 1939-40 and it ran until 1945-46, with the regular Football League returning in 1946-47. Leicester was credited with winning their division in the 1941-42 campaign.
10. The players with the top-10 official appearances for Leicester are Graham Cross, 600; Adam Black, 557; Hughie Adcock, 460; Mark Wallington, 460; Steve Walsh, 450; Arthur Chandler, 419; Kasper Schmeichel, 415; John Sjoberg, 414; Mal Griffiths, 409; and Steve Whitworth, 401. It should be noted that goalkeeper Kasper Schmeichel was still playing with the club as of April 2021.

CHAPTER 11:

EUROPE AND BEYOND

QUIZ TIME!

1. How many major European competitions have the Foxes competed in?

    a. 1
    b. 3
    c. 5
    d. 7

2. Leicester reached the quarterfinals of the 2016-17 UEFA Champions League.

    a. True
    b. False

3. Which was the first club Leicester faced in an international competition?

    a. VfB Stuttgart
    b. Granada CF
    c. Atlético Madrid
    d. Glenavon FC

4. Who is the Foxes' top scorer in the UEFA Champions League?

   a. Andy King
   b. Jamie Vardy
   c. Riyad Mahrez
   d. Ken Keyworth

5. What was the first European competition the Foxes competed in?

   a. UEFA Champions League
   b. European Cup Winners' Cup
   c. Anglo-Italian Cup
   d. UEFA Europa Cup

6. Who was the first player to score a goal in an international competition for the team?

   a. Colin Appleton
   b. James Walsh
   c. Ken Keyworth
   d. John King

7. Leicester has lost 17 matches in UEFA tournaments.

   a. True
   b. False

8. How many times did the Foxes compete in the Anglo-Italian Cup?

   a. 7
   b. 2

c. 5
d. 3

9. Which team eliminated Leicester in the 1972-73 Texaco Cup quarterfinals?

   a. Norwich City FC
   b. Heart of Midlothian FC
   c. Ayr United
   d. Ipswich Town FC

10. What was the first season Leicester competed in a major European tournament?

   a. 1999-00
   b. 1997-98
   c. 1961-62
   d. 1957-58

11. How many goals did Riyad Mahrez score in the UEFA Champions League with Leicester?

   a. 12
   b. 7
   c. 4
   d. 3

12. The Foxes have scored 43 goals in all UEFA tournaments.

   a. True
   b. False

13. Which club did Leicester play in the first round of the 2000-01 UEFA Cup?

a. Red Star Belgrade
b. Deportivo Alavés
c. Udinese Calcio
d. Lierse SK

14. Leicester did not play which side in the 1975-76 Anglo-Scottish Cup?

    a. West Bromwich Albion
    b. Hull City FC
    c. Mansfield Town FC
    d. Bristol City FC

15. How many games have the Foxes won in major UEFA competitions?

    a. 17
    b. 14
    c. 11
    d. 8

16. Leicester waited 36 years between its first and second appearance in a major European tournament.

    a. True
    b. False

17. Which club did the Foxes not play in the group stage of the 2020-21 UEFA Europa League?

    a. SC Braga
    b. SK Slavia Prague
    c. FC Zorya Luhansk
    d. AEK Athens

18. How many games has Leicester played in major UEFA tournaments?
    a. 37
    b. 26
    c. 21
    d. 18
19. Which club eliminated the Foxes in the 2016-17 UEFA Champions League quarterfinal?
    a. Inter Milan
    b. FC Porto
    c. Club Brugge
    d. Atlético Madrid
20. The Foxes qualified for the 1961-62 European Cup Winners' Cup by winning the FA Cup the year prior.
    a. True
    b. False

QUIZ ANSWERS

1. C – 5
2. A – True
3. D – Glenavon FC
4. C – Riyad Mahrez
5. B – European Cup Winners' Cup
6. B – James Walsh
7. B – False
8. D – 3
9. A – Norwich City FC
10. C – 1961-62
11. C – 4
12. B – False
13. A – Red Star Belgrade
14. D – Bristol City FC
15. C – 11
16. A – True
17. B – SK Slavia Prague
18. B – 26
19. D – Atlético Madrid
20. B – False

DID YOU KNOW?

1. Leicester has competed in five major European tournaments as of 2020-21. Their first came in 1961-62 when the Foxes took part in the European Cup Winners' Cup. This was followed by appearances in the 1997-98 and 2000-01 UEFA Cup and the 2016-17 European Champions League. They also competed in the 2020-21 Europa League and have also entered minor tournaments, including the Anglo-Italian Cup, the Anglo-Scottish Cup, and the Texaco Cup.

2. The Foxes met semi-pro Glenavon of Northern Ireland in the preliminary round of the 1961-62 European Cup Winners' Cup and won 7-2 on aggregate. They were 3-1 winners at home and 4-1 winners away. They then faced Atlético Madrid in the first round and were downed 3-1 on aggregate following a 1-1 home draw and 2-1 away defeat. Atlético then went on to win the competition. The Foxes had qualified for the event by losing the FA Cup to Tottenham Hotspur, who also won the First Division that season and were already entered into the European Cup.

3. It was 36 years before the club played a major tournament in Europe again. The Foxes qualified for the 1997-98 UEFA Cup due to winning the League Cup in 1996-97. They played Atlético Madrid again and were edged 2-1 in Spain in the first leg and beaten 2-0 at home in the second

leg for a 4-1 aggregate defeat. Ian Marshall was the lone Leicester goal-scorer.

4. The next European appearance was the 2000-01 UEFA Cup, which the Foxes qualified for by winning the League Cup in 1999-2000. The Foxes were matched against Red Star Belgrade of Serbia in the first round. Due to possible civil unrest in the nation because of an upcoming election, the second leg was moved to Vienna, Austria. The teams drew the first leg in Leicester 1-1 and Belgrade won the second leg 3-1 in Vienna to advance 4-2 on aggregate.

5. After winning the 2015-16 Premier League, Leicester qualified for the 2016-17 European Champions League. They were drawn in Group G with Porto, Club Brugge, and Copenhagen and won the group with 4 wins, 1 draw, and 1 loss. The Foxes lost 2-1 away to Sevilla in the next round and were 2-0 victors at home to advance 3-2 on aggregate. They were then eliminated by Atlético Madrid for the third time in a European tournament after losing the first leg of the quarterfinals 1-0 away and drawing the second leg 1-1 at home.

6. As a result of finishing fifth in the 2019-20 Premier League, Leicester qualified for the group stage of the 2020-21 Europa League. They were placed in Group G with Braga, AEK Athens, and Zorya Luhansk and advanced to the knockout stage by posting 4 wins, 1 draw, and 1 loss to top the group. However, they were beaten by Slavia Prague in the round-of-32 after a 0-0

away draw in the first leg and a 2-0 home defeat in the second leg.

7. The Anglo-Italian Cup was a tournament for Italian end English teams that didn't qualify for major UEFA tournaments. It was played as a pro event from 1970 to 1973 and again from 1992 to 1996. The Foxes entered the competition in 1972 and faced Cagliari and Atalanta. They lost their away games and won at home to finish third out of six English teams and were eliminated.

8. The Foxes played in the 1992-93 and 1993-94 Anglo-Italian Cup events but were eliminated in the preliminary rounds both times. In 1992-93, they beat Grimsby Town but lost to Newcastle United and the next season they were beaten by Peterborough United and West Bromwich Albion.

9. The Texaco Cup operated for five seasons from 1970-71 to 1974-75 and involved clubs from England, Scotland, and Ireland that didn't qualify for major European competitions. The Irish and Northern Irish teams withdrew after 1971-72 and formed the separate Texaco (All-Ireland) Cup. Leicester played in 1972-73 and eliminated Dundee United in a penalty shootout following two draws. They then lost a penalty shootout to Norwich City after each team won 2-0 at home. The next season, the Foxes beat Ayr United drawing by drawing 1-1 in Scotland and winning 2-0 at home. However, they were eliminated by Dundee United after losing 1-0 in Dundee and drawing 1-1at home.

10. The Texaco Cup was renamed the Anglo-Scottish Cup in 1975-76 and converted to a group-stage format. Leicester was placed in Group 2 of the English Qualifiers West Bromwich Albion, Hull City, and Mansfield Town. However, they managed just 1 win, 1 draw, and 1 odd and were eliminated after the group games.

CHAPTER 12:

TOP SCORERS

QUIZ TIME!

1. Who is the Foxes' all-time top scorer?
    a. Arthur Rowley
    b. Ernie Hine
    c. Arthur Chandler
    d. Jamie Vardy
2. Jack Bowers was the first Leicester player to win a Golden Boot award.
    a. True
    b. False
3. Who was the first player to lead Leicester in scoring in the Football League?
    a. Willie McArthur
    b. Billy Dorrell
    c. David Skea
    d. Roddy McLeod

4. How many goals did Matty Fryatt score to lead the Foxes in the 2008-09 League One season?
   a. 15
   b. 19
   c. 24
   d. 27
5. Who won a 1984-85 Golden Boot award?
   a. Gary Lineker
   b. Alan Smith
   c. Jim Melrose
   d. Tommy English
6. What is the most goals a Leicester player has scored in a single season?
   a. 34
   b. 37
   c. 44
   d. 49
7. Archie Gardiner scored 4 goals in his Leicester debut.
   a. True
   b. False
8. How many goals did Arthur Rowley score in all competitions for the Foxes?
   a. 243
   b. 265
   c. 277
   d. 280

9. Who led the 2009-10 domestic league season in scoring?

    a. Craig King
    b. DJ Campbell
    c. Barry Hayles
    d. Martyn Waghorn

10. What player holds Leicester's longest scoring streak with at least one goal in 11 consecutive games?

    a. Riyad Mahrez
    b. Iain Hume
    c. Arthur Chandler
    d. Jamie Vardy

11. Johnny Duncan scored 6 goals in one game against which club?

    a. Port Vale FC
    b. Wigan Athletic
    c. Blackpool FC
    d. AFC Bournemouth

12. Jamie Vardy scored 25 goals to win the 2019-20 Premier League Golden Boot award.

    a. True
    b. False

13. Who led the Foxes in scoring in their first Premier League season?

    a. Julian Joachim
    b. Phil Gee

c. Iwan Roberts
d. Emile Heskey

14. How many goals did Arthur Chandler score in all competitions with Leicester?

a. 303
b. 281
c. 273
d. 258

15. How many different Foxes' players have won the second-tier Golden Boot award?

a. 3
b. 6
c. 8
d. 9

16. Arthur Rowley holds the current club record for most goals scored from the penalty spot in all competitions with 41.

a. True
b. False

17. Which player led the squad with 17 goals in the 2002-03 domestic league season.

a. Brian Deane
b. Tomi Petrescu
c. Muzzy Izzet
d. Paul Dickov

18. How many goals did Ernie Hine score in all competitions with the Foxes?

    a. 156
    b. 184
    c. 215
    d. 255

19. Who won the 1955-56 Second Division Golden Boot award?

    a. Jimmy Goodfellow
    b. Arthur Rowley
    c. Willie Gardiner
    d. Jack Lee

20. Gary Lineker led the Foxes in scoring in six consecutive seasons.

    a. True
    b. False

QUIZ ANSWERS

1. C – Arthur Chandler
2. B – False
3. C – David Skea
4. D – 27
5. A – Gary Lineker
6. C – 44
7. A – True
8. B – 265
9. B – Martyn Waghorn
10. D – Jamie Vardy
11. A – Port Vale FC
12. B – False
13. C – Iwan Roberts
14. C – 273
15. B – 6
16. A – True
17. D – Paul Dickov
18. A – 156
19. C – Willie Gardiner
20. B – False

DID YOU KNOW?

1. As of April 2021, the following players were the top-20 scorers in club history. All players hail from the UK and it should be noted that Jamie Vardy is still playing with the club: Arthur Chandler, 273; Arthur Rowley, 265; Ernie Hine, 156; Jamie Vardy, 144; Derek Hines, 117; Arthur Lochhead, 114; Gary Lineker, 103; Mike Stringfellow, 97; Johnny Duncan, 95; Jimmy Walsh, 92; Jack Lee, 84; Alan Smith, 84; Frank Worthington, 78; Mal Griffiths, 76; Ken Keyworth, 76; Danny Liddle, 71; Arthur Maw, 64; Matty Fryatt, 62; Andy King, 62; Steve Walsh, 62; Steve Lynex, 60; David Nugent, 59; Fred Shinton, 58; and Jack Bowers, 56.

2. Leicester players have led their divisions in scoring on several occasions. The following are players who have won a Golden Boot while playing with the side. Top-tier First Division: Gary Lineker, 28 goals in 1984-85; Premier League: Jamie Vardy, 23 goals in 2019-20; Second-tier Second Division: David Skea, 31 goals in 1894-95; Arthur Chandler, 38 goals in 1924-25; Jack Bowers, 35 goals in 1936-37; Arthur Rowley, 41 goals in 1952-53; Willie Gardiner, 35 goals in 1955-56; Arthur Rowley, 44 goals in 1956-57; and Gary Lineker, 26 goals in 1982-83.

3. Arthur Chandler made 419 appearances for Leicester from 1923 to 1935 to rank sixth on the games-played list. He joined from Queens Park Rangers and became the

team's all-time top scorer with 273 goals. He owns club records for the most goals in a top-flight season with 34, which he managed twice, and the most hat tricks with 17. He also scored 6 goals against Portsmouth in 1928 to share the team mark for most goals in a game. Chandler is Leicester's oldest goal-scorer at the age of 39 years and 34 days, but he never scored a goal on a penalty kick as both his attempts were saved. He helped the team win the Second Division crown in 1924-25 and finish as First Division runners-up in 1928-29.

4. There must be something about the name Arthur at Leicester because Arthur Rowley notched 265 goals in 321 games from 1950 to 1958. He arrived from Fulham, scored in his debut, and helped the side win the Second Division in 1953-54. The Foxes were relegated after a season in the top tier but won the Second Division again in 1956-57. Rowley moved to Shrewsbury in 1958. He finished his career with 434 goals in 619 outings to set the record for most goals in English club football. Rowley was also a cricket player and holds the Foxes' record for most goals in a season with 44 in 42 league contests.

5. Third on the club's all-time scoring list is English international Ernie Hine with 156 goals, which is a full 109 behind second-place Arthur Rowley, but Hine achieved the feat in 259 games. He's also the top goal-scorer in the history of Barnsley with 131 goals and totaled 287 career league goals. Hine arrived at Filbert Street in 1926 and by 1932 had joined Huddersfield Town. He scored twice on

his Leicester debut and helped the squad finish as First Division runners-up in 1928-29.

6. The only top-10 scorer still with the club was 34-year-old English international Jamie Vardy, who scored 144 goals in 341 outings. The striker joined in May 2012 from non-league Fleetwood Town, where he had notched 31 league goals in his first season and was named the club's Player of the Year. The Foxes paid a reported non-League record transfer fee of £1 million for him and Vardy helped the side win the Championship League in 2013-2014. He scored in 11 straight games in 2015-16 to set a new Premier League record and helped Leicester win the title. Vardy also took home the Premier League Player of the Season and FWA Footballer of the Year awards that year. He followed up in 2019-20 by winning the top-flight Golden Boot with 23 goals to become the oldest player to win the award.

7. After spending his youth with Derby County, center-forward Derek Hines began his pro career with the Foxes from 1948 to 1961 before joining Shrewsbury Town. He formed a prolific striking partnership with Arthur Rowley and helped the side hoist the Second Division title in 1953-54 and 1956-57. Hines registered 117 goals in 317 outings, with 4 of them coming in a game against Aston Villa in November 1958. He returned to Filbert Street in the 1970s as a youth team coach.

8. The third Arthur to make the club's top-six scorers is Arthur Lochhead of Scotland. He joined in 1925 from Manchester United and proceeded to tally 114 times in 320 contests before hanging up his boots in 1943. He helped the side win runners-up medals in the First Division in 1928-29 when he netted 13 league goals and then managed Leicester between 1934 and 1936. Lochhead enjoyed his best scoring campaign in 1927-28 with 17 strikes in 44 appearances in all competitions.

9. English international Gary Lineker became one of the greatest strikers in the world after kicking off his career with hometown Leicester. The former Leicester youth player notched 103 goals in 216 games between 1978 and 1985 before joining Everton. He won a First and Second Division Golden Boot with the team and led it in scoring for four straight seasons. Lineker helped the squad top the Second Division in 1979-80, and he eventually went on to score 48 goals in 80 contests for England. He also played with Barcelona and Tottenham Hotspur and in Japan, won numerous team and individual awards, is a member of the English Football Hall of Fame, and is currently a top television pundit in the UK.

10. Winger Mike Stringfellow began his career with Mansfield Town in 1957 as a schoolboy and made his pro debut just after turning 17 years old. He notched 12 goals in 65 matches before the Foxes bought his services for a reported £25,000 in January 1962 to set a new transfer record at the time for an 18-year-old. Stringfellow helped

the side reach the 1962-63 FA Cup final and scored in the 1963-64 League Cup final in Leicester's 4-3 aggregate victory over Stoke City. He suffered a serious knee injury in 1968 and joined non-league Nuneaton Borough in 1975. Stringfellow played 370 official games for Leicester and netted 97 goals.

CONCLUSION

The Leicester FC story is well into its second century, and the club is just as entertaining now as it has been since being formed. You've just read the history of this famous outfit from the very beginning right up till the 2020-21 Premier League campaign.

We hope you've enjoyed taking a trip back through time to re-live the glorious, and not-so-glorious, events that have shaped this magnificent team. We also appreciate the fact that even the most loyal and passionate fans may have learned something new along the way.

After reading the 12 lighthearted and entertaining trivia chapters, filled with a wide variety of quiz questions and "Did You Know" facts, you should feel more confident than ever when it comes to accepting trivia challenges from fellow Leicester and soccer fans.

We've attempted to include as many of the club's most popular players and managers as possible and provide fans with an assortment of informative end educational facts and trivia, regarding Leicester's successes, failures, transfers, statistics, records, and more.

Of course, with the club being born in 1884 it was impossible to include everybody, and we sincerely apologize if we've omitted any of your favorites.

We also hope you'll be inclined to share this Leicester trivia and fact publication with other soccer fans to help spread the word about the Foxes' glorious history.

The club now knows what it takes to capture a Premier League crown, and fans should expect the side to seriously challenge for another one in the not-too-distant future.

Thank you kindly for being a loyal Leicester supporter and for re-living the club's adventures by reading our latest trivia book.

Made in the USA
Coppell, TX
24 February 2023